Dan Abnett
Kev Hopgood

Darkblade™

A BLACK LIBRARY PUBLICATION

Darkblade ™

SCRIPT **Dan Abnett**

ART/LETTERS **Kev Hopgood**

EDITORS **Marc Gascoigne & Andy Jones**

COVER **Wayne Reynolds**

PRODUCTION **Marc Gascoigne**

A BLACK LIBRARY PUBLICATION

First published in Great Britain in 2000 by Games Workshop Publishing, Willow Rd, Lenton, Nottingham NG7 2WS, UK

Distributed by Amalgamated Book Services, Royal Star Arcade, High Street, Maidstone, Kent, ME14 1JL, UK

A CIP record for this book is available from the British Library.

Printed in Great Britain.

INTERNET AND ONLINE STORE

http://www.blacklibrary.co.uk

http://www.games-workshop.com

NOW HEAR THE TALE OF *MALUS DARKBLADE*, DARK ELF, BLIGHTED ONE, TOUCHED BY DAEMONS.

HEAR OF HIM AND HIS COLD-BLOODED STEED *SPITE*, AND THE YEAR OF THE FOUL CURSE OF *TZ'ARKAN*.

HEAR FIRST, THE DIN OF CONFLICT ...

SLAUGHTER! SLAUGHTER THEM ALL! FOR THE GLORY OF KHAINE!

DarkBlade

PART ONE

SCRIPT: DAN ABNETT

ART: KEV HOPGOOD

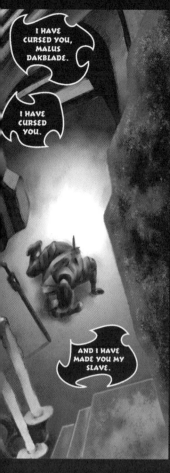

Next - The Treasure of the Beastmen.

NOW HEAR MORE OF THE TALE OF *MALUS DARKBLADE*, DARK ELF, CURSED BY DAEMONS.

HEAR OF HIS UNWILLING QUEST TO RETRIEVE FIVE RELICS OF UNHOLY POWER FOR THE BESTIAL ABOMINATION *TZARKAN*.

HEAR NOW, THE STORY OF THE *FIRST* RELIC ...

BRRRRAAAARGHHHHH!

DARKBLADE
PART TWO

SCRIPT: DAN ARNETT   ART: KEV HOPGOOD

NEXT- THE LABYRINTH

A MAGIC LABYRINTH, MALUS... DEVISED BY ERADORIUS IN HIS DOTAGE, BEFORE DISEASE AND INFIRMITY TOOK HIM OFF. IT REPRESENTS THE TWISTED RECESSES OF HIS RAVING PSYCHE. AND THE WORST OF IT IS-
JUST TELL ME HOW I CAN FIND MY WAY AROUND, DAEMON! I DON'T WANT TO GET LOST IN HERE !
WE WILL LEAVE A TRAIL, MALUS... A THREAD...
VERY WELL.
HOW MUCH LONGER ? I CANNOT TELL IF IT'S BEEN DAYS OR MERELY HOURS. THIS PLACE SMELLS OF DEATH AND MADNESS !
NOT FAR NOW, MALUS.
WHAT WAS THAT ? A SNUFFLING, A GRUNTING ? I THOUGHT YOU SAID THIS PLACE WAS DEAD, DAEMON !
I SAID ERADORIUS WAS DEAD.

CRAARGHH...!

KHAINE'S BLOODY INNARDS!

SMATCHHH!

BUT HE DIDN'T LEAVE HIS LABYRINTH UNGUARDED.

A BULL-MAN!

YES, QUITE THE FASHION AS LABYRINTH GUARDS IN ERADORIUS'S DAY...

DAMN YOUR DEAMON THREAD! IT BINDS MY ARM!

DON'T LET IT BREAK, MALUS, OR WE ARE LOST IN HERE!

AGHHH! HE FEELS NOTHING OF MY BLOWS!

IS WHAT WE CAME FOR ? THIS PIECE OF BRASS SCRAP ?
GRAAAAAAAAAAAA!
IT IS THE SECOND TALISMAN. THE IDOL OF KOLKUTH. WELL DONE, MALUS.
EH ?
NOW YOU HAVE TAKEN THE TALISMAN, ERADORIUS'S ENCHANTMENTS ARE CANCELLED. THE TOWER IS DESTROYING ITSELF. IT IS SICK OF THE DARK MAGIC.
I KNOW HOW IT FEELS ...
DARKBLADE RETURNS IN ISSUE 5 WITH "FLESH AND BLOOD"

HEAR TOLD MORE OF THE TALE OF *MALUS DARKBLADE*, CURSED WARRIOR, DARK ELF, PUPPET OF CHAOS.

HEAR HOW HE WAS *ENSLAVED* TO SEARCH FOR FIVE RELICS OF UNHOLY POWER, ENSLAVED BY THE FOUL DAEMON *TZARKAN*.

AND HEAR NOW, THE STORY OF THE *THIRD* RELIC...

AT THE EDGE OF THE WASTELAND LIES *VAELGOR KEEP*, A WAY STATION FOR DARK ELF RAIDING PARTIES.

ONE BITTER NIGHT IN WINTER, A RETURNING WARBAND WERE CELEBRATING THEIR TRIUMPHS.

DRINK DEEP, MY KIN! THE FABLED *DAGGER OF TORXUS* IS OURS! OUR NAMES WILL BE INSCRIBED ON THE ROLL OF HONOUR IN KHAINE'S OWN TEMPLE ON OUR RETURN!

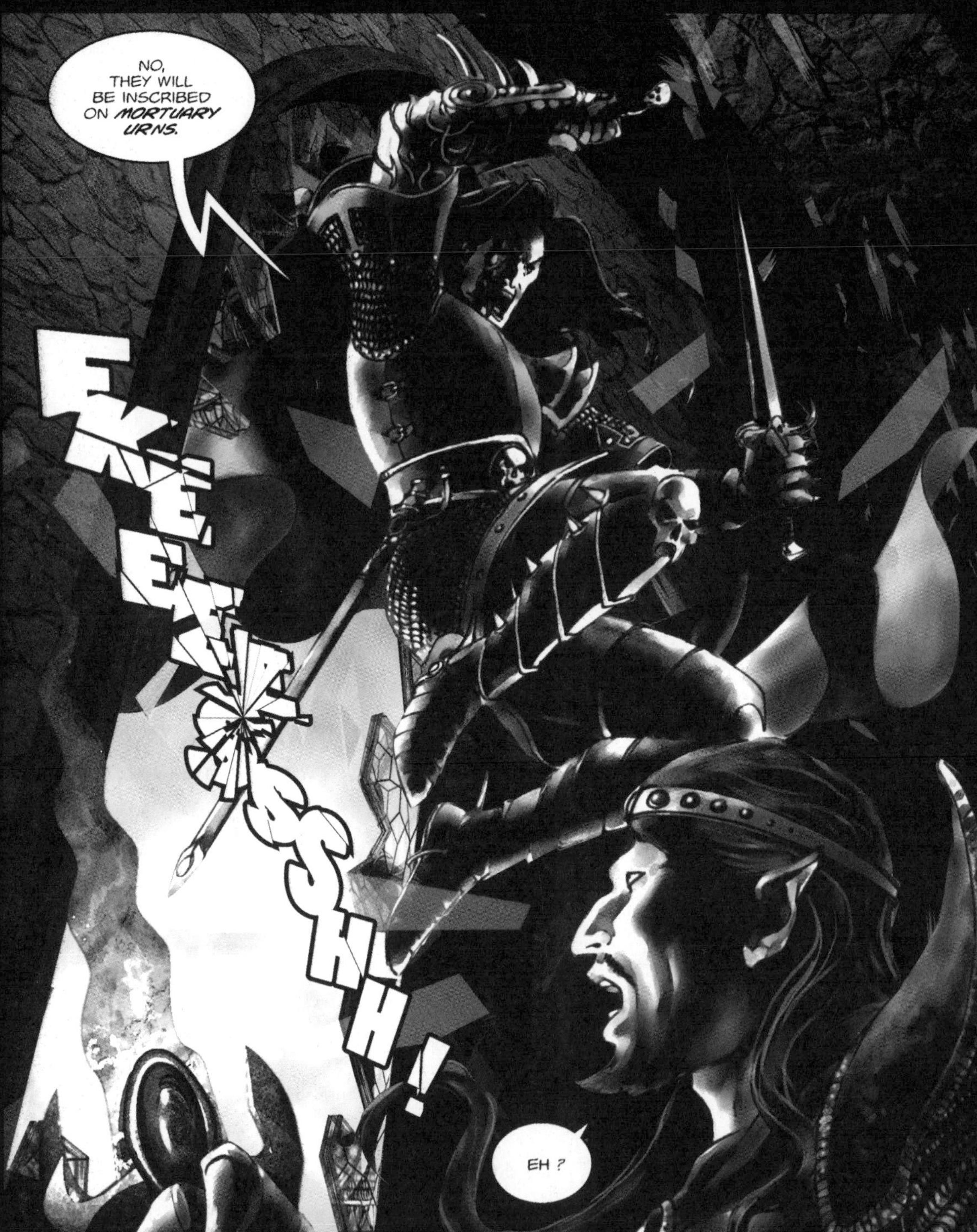

DarkBlade

PART FOUR

SCRIPT : DAN ABNETT

ART : KEV HOPGOOD

NEXT - HELLFIRE

DarkBlade

Part Five

LISTEN AS THE DREAD STORY OF *MALUS DARKBLADE* NOW UNFOLDS.

WHOEVER LIVES HERE, DAEMON ... HAS QUITE AN APPETITE.

KNOW FIRST THAT HE WAS *CURSED* TO SEEK OUT FIVE RELICS OF UNHOLY POWER FOR THE FILTHY DAEMON *TZARKAN*, WHO LIVES INSIDE HIS SOUL.

THEN LET'S HOPE HE'S SLEEPING, MALUS.

THEN HEAR THE TALE OF THE *FOURTH* RELIC.

SOMEWHERE IN THESE DARK GULLIES LIES THE LOST WARPSWORD OF KHAINE. WE'RE NOT LEAVING UNTIL YOU'VE FOUND IT.

SCRIPT: DAN ABNETT ✳ ART: KEV HOPGOOD

WINTER HAD COME AROUND AGAIN, AS COLD AND BITTER AS THE WINTER BEFORE WHEN MALUS DARKBLADES' ARROGANCE HAD LED HIM TO THE RESTING PLACE OF THE BOUND DAEMON *T'ZARKAN*...

... AND THE *CURSE* HAD COME UPON HIM.

HE HAD BEEN GIVEN FOUR SEASONS TO RECOVER *FIVE RELICS OF DARK POWER*, AND RETURN WITH THEM OR HIS LIFE WOULD BE FORFEIT.

THOSE FIVE TASKS HAD BEEN DEMANDING, BUT NOW THE *HARDEST* TASK OF ALL REMAINED...

... THE JOURNEY BACK ACROSS THE FROZEN WASTES TO FIND THE DAEMONS' PRISON BEFORE THE LAST FEW DAYS OF THE YEAR TICKED AWAY AND TOOK HIS *LIFE* WITH THEM.

BY THE TIME HE REACHED THE DARK GORGE THAT LEAD TO THE OLD TEMPLE WHERE THE DAEMON WAS BOUND, ONLY A *SINGLE DAY* REMAINED OF HIS ALLOTTED TIME.

THE BONES OF HIS KINSMEN LAY WHERE HE HAD LEFT THEM..

COLD WINTER GALES SLICED DOWN FROM THE LATITUDES WHERE ICE NEVER MELTS.

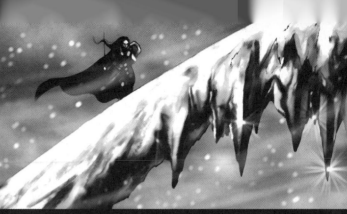

WELL, DAEMON, I MADE IT ...

SO YOU DID, MALUS ...

AND I HAVE YOUR DAMNED TREASURES... THE OCTAGRAM OF PRAAN, THE IDOL OF KOLKUTH, THE DAGGER OF TORXUS, THE WARPSWORD OF KHAINE...

... THE AMULET OF VAUROG.

NOW LISTEN WELL, MALUS... THIS IS ALL THAT REMAINS FOR YOU TO DO...

LAST DAY TO PREPARE THE RITUAL ...

... SIGILS WERE INSCRIBED, PUNGENT FIRES LIT...

... LITANIES RECITED FROM STONE TABLETS SMOOTH WITH AGE...

... AND THEN THE LAST CONJURINGS, CHANTED IN A TONGUE THAT HAD NOT BEEN SPOKEN FOR *NINE COLD CENTURIES.*

THE MAGICAL SHACKLES THAT HAD BOUND TZ'ARKAN FOR SO LONG WERE NOW WORKING LOOSE.

SOMEHOW, MALUS WAS NOT SURPRISED THAT THE DAEMON WAS ESCAPING FROM HIM, AND NOT THE STONE.

TZ'ARKAN WAS FREE ONCE MORE.

DREADFULLY WOUNDED BY THE VERY RELICS THAT HAD FREED HIM, THE DAEMON FLED.

MALUS WAS ALONE AT LAST.

THE DAEMON HAD FLED, TAKING PART OF THE *DARK ELFS' SOUL* WITH HIM.

BUT EVEN AS HE ROSE, MALUS KNEW THERE HAD BEEN A PRICE TO PAY. HE FELT AN EMPTINESS, A *HOLLOWNESS...*

NOW MALUS DARKBLADE HAD A *NEW* QUEST, ONE HE KNEW MIGHT TAKE HIM TO THE ENDS OF THE WORLD AND THE EDGES OF HIS LIFESPAN.

HOWEVER, HE SWORE HE WOULD NOT FAIL. TZ'ARKAN WOULD NOT ESCAPE.

BUT THAT IS, OF COURSE, *ANOTHER* TALE ENTIRELY.

END OF BOOK ONE.

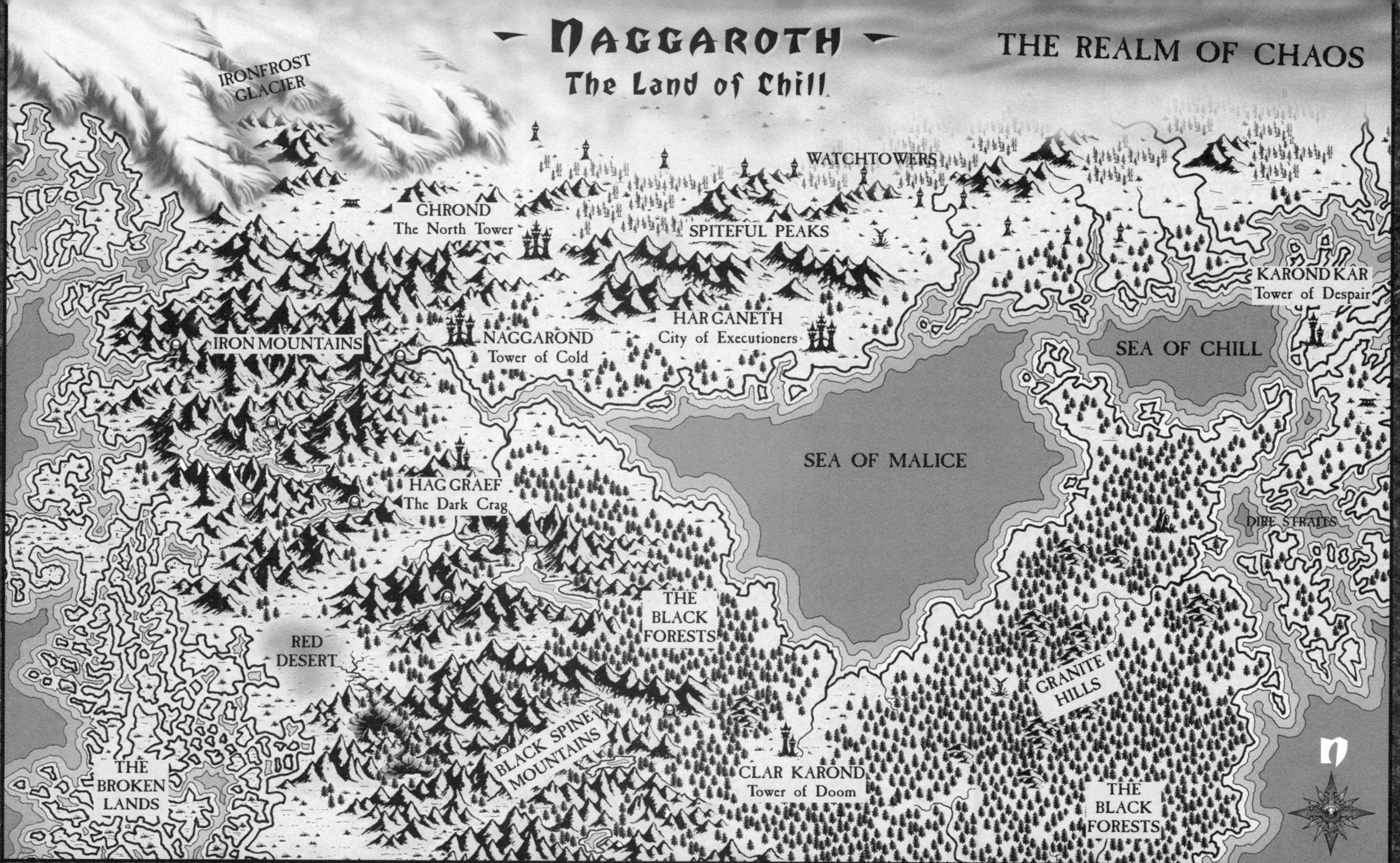

NAGGAROTH
The Land of Chill

THE REALM OF CHAOS

IRONFROST GLACIER

WATCHTOWERS

SPITEFUL PEAKS

GHROND
The North Tower

NAGGAROND
Tower of Cold

HAR GANETH
City of Executioners

KAROND KAR
Tower of Despair

SEA OF CHILL

DIRE STRAITS

SEA OF MALICE

GRANITE HILLS

THE BLACK FORESTS

IRON MOUNTAINS

HAG GRAEF
The Dark Crag

THE BLACK FORESTS

CLAR KAROND
Tower of Doom

THE BLACK SPINE MOUNTAINS

RED DESERT

THE BROKEN LANDS